SWEDISH DEATH CLEANING WORKBOOK

A MANUAL, PLANNER AND GUIDEBOOK TO HELP YOU ORGANISE AND DECLUTTER

LIMITLESS PUBLISHING

PREAMBLE

One of the prevailing challenges that affect actions on so many levels is the over-saturation of information. One doesn't have to go far in their quest to know more about a subject before they are bombarded with lots of information about it. This is also the case with Swedish death cleaning; there is more than enough data on the subject that can get one overwhelmed.

This workbook, however, is unique, as its purpose is to arrange an exhaustive guide for you to undertake the Swedish death cleaning exercise effectively. It is interactive and aims at inspiring guidance and motivation, amongst other things. In addition, the reader will get a deeper insight into various topics on the overall subject.

In order to effectively carry out the Swedish death cleaning exercise, one would have to be familiar with its history, origin, and practice; other concepts, such as its definition, descriptions, and societal misconceptions, would have to be thoroughly discussed. This vital information would assist in the mental formation of the right ideas and considerations about the subject, which will, in turn, aid the reader's navigation through each process.

Another important take from this workbook would be what exactly one should expect before starting and while embarking on the exercise. Guidelines and insight would be offered to aid with mental, emotional, and physical preparedness before getting on to the exercise. Once the body and mind of the reader are adequately prepared, taking the necessary steps would be much easier and with little or no hassle.

The reader will be furnished with a step-by-step guide to aid with formulating a routine, leading to a stress-free cleaning exercise. The phase guide would include what to do, whom to do it with, how to classify items, how and where to dispose of items no longer wanted, how to sell or resell surplus items and goods, and so on. A number of examples and short stories have been added to help with clearer illustrations. Each of them will carry a message to meet the core yearnings of this workbook, as stated earlier. Each read would be rich, exciting, and inspiring.

In the end, the reader will be furnished with a timeline to aid in carrying out the exercise within a definite period. This important gesture will aid in eliminating inaction or procrastination, time wastage, and needless delays. All these put together will not do the reader any good if their sheer commitment, perseverance, and determination are not stirred and applied throughout the exercise. Because the Swedish death cleaning is accompanied by its unique challenges, it can be a fun exercise if done correctly and with a bit of spice. Once the reader commits to following the guidelines provided in this book, it would be needless to say that success can be guaranteed.

The much-needed commitment, accompanied by desire and action, will yield tremendous results, leading to a robust, fulfilled life. There is no doubt that once a person's mind is made up, there is nothing that can stand in their way of achieving their desired feat except themselves. Therefore, the reader must pull all the stops and give their best as they venture into performing the Swedish death cleaning.

Cheers.

CHAPTER 1

SWEDISH DEATH CLEANING

"Have you heard of the Swedish death cleaning?" Ashley asked her friend, Jon, as she took a sip from her glass of wine while adjusting herself on the sofa in the VIP lounge. Jon kept his gaze on the dance floor below while he swung from side to side to the music playing in the background.

"Jon, focus!" Ashley said, "you seem a bit distant. Is your wine too strong for you?"

"Oh, I'm sorry, I'm so loving the whole ambiance of this place," Jon replied with a sheepish smile and reached for his glass of wine. "Swedish death cleaning? You're not dying, are you?" he asked with a serious disposition.

"Of course not. I just heard my mom talking about it this morning. Trust me. I reacted the same way," Ashley said as she gulped more wine.

"Well..." Jon said, "I've never heard of it, but it does sound like some voodoo stuff coming off the Swedish isle."

Ashley laughed as she leaned further on the sofa. "I see your brain has been taken over by the wine already. I hadn't heard of it until this morning, but it's definitely not what you just described."

"It may not be all that, but it does sound like it!" Jon said, "and even if I'm wrong, I guarantee it is some death-related thingy. Sounds like something your mum should stay away from unless she has some kind of a death wish."

Answer the following question by ticking the appropriate boxes.

Question 1

Have you ever heard of the Swedish death cleaning?

Yes _________ No ________

Question 2

Where did you first learn about the Swedish death cleaning?

From a family member

From hearsay

From the Web

Other

Tick the option(s) that best labels your opinion about the Swedish death cleaning

I think Swedish death cleaning is a well-thought-out scam.

I think Swedish death cleaning is a Swedish ritual solely practiced for the Swedes.

I think Swedish death cleaning is a pious practice.

I see Swedish death cleaning as unnecessary. It is a total waste of time and energy.

I think Swedish death cleaning is a required exercise for decluttering and letting go.

I see Swedish death cleaning as a practice meant for the old and/or dying.

Other (Please state below)

The Swedish death cleaning or purge was gotten from the Swedish word *döstädning*. This is a mishmash of the words *"dö"* (connoting death) and *"städning"* (connoting purge). The exercise has been misunderstood by many, partly due to a lack of proper information about the subject and the word "death" included in it.

Swedish death cleaning is the act of bringing together one's life with the intention of getting rid of clutter, purging any and all things that up till now were essential but are not anymore. It is the unhurried journey towards the removal, elimination, and doing away with disproportionate belongings, things that utterly lost their relevance in one's life as time passed. Typically, the Swedish death cleaning method has been known to birth liberty from hoarded garbage and stacked up belongings that do not need to be retained.

One notable benefit of embarking on such an exercise, particularly for the aged, is that in their eventual death, members of their family or loved ones left behind would have little belongings to handle or manage. This ultimately implies that the Swedish death cleaning does not only benefit the participant but others who they cherish.

As important and beneficial as the Swedish death cleaning is, many people are still skeptical about embarking on the exercise.

Have you contemplated carrying out the Swedish death cleaning? If yes, please tick any one or more reasons below why you may hold back from carrying out the exercise:

Why I'm holding back

The exercise is too technical. I need a professional to do it for me.

The exercise is too burdensome. It might overwhelm me at some point.

The exercise is time-consuming. I just don't have time for it.

I am unsure about a lot. I am of two minds. What do I discard? What do I keep?

I feel every item I have is important. Unnecessary items might prove invaluable in the future. Who knows?

I hold gift items so dearly. Why discard them, even when they are no longer valuable?

The exercise is expensive. My items cost a lot of money, and I don't see why I should discard them.

I feel like what I currently have might break down one day. That's why I stocked up on duplicates.

My children and grandchildren might need those items when I'm long gone. Why discard them now?

Other (please show below)

____

____

From the aforementioned list, clearly show below the three utmost reasons that have kept you from carrying out the Swedish death cleaning.

-

-

-

Highlight below how you think you can overcome the three aforementioned reasons.

-

-

-

-

-

What Swedish Death Cleaning is

"Mom, I'm telling you, don't do it!" Ashley said to her mother with hands akimbo as they conversed in the kitchen area, "I heard this Swedish Death cleaning stuff is nothing but garbage." She added.

Ashley's mother looked at her with shock on her face. "How so?" she asked.

"Well," Ashley began, "people come up with just about anything these days to get into your pocket. What if it is some religious hoax? She added.

"Believe me, honey, Swedish death cleaning is nothing of the sort. Where did you get such information from?" her mom enquired.

"That's not important. My point is that I'm concerned about you trying to do this exercise. Have you thought of the money it will demand? Do we know any Swedish clergy to call? What about the cost of hiring a professional Swedish death cleaner? And I heard it is an exercise for people on the brink of death!" Ashley said with obvious irritation in her voice.

Her mom laughed out loud, "Darling, none of what you said is an accurate description of Swedish death cleaning. In fact, most of what you pointed out is quite the opposite. We do not need to hire a pro or call a Swedish clergy. The exercise isn't as expensive as you might think, and I'm not dying soon." She said.

Ashley looked at her mom with relief in her eyes, "okay. So, what is this Swedish death cleaning?"

As stated earlier in this chapter, the Swedish death cleaning or purge has been misunderstood by many. Here, we will attempt to clearly spell out what the exercise entails as this will help shed light, leaving no grey areas. Furthermore, doing this will aid with accepting the act unreservedly.

- It consists of Letting go

Typically, important items can gradually lose their worth and become dispensable over time. Instead of these items adding value to one's life, they begin to take away value, becoming serious liabilities, which could even become harmful in some cases. Furthermore, these now dispensable items may require unaffordable amounts of energy and resources for their maintenance alone. Such items have to be let go and done away with.

Do you have items within your living space that can now be referred to as valueless? List some of these items below that you feel should be let go in the shortest possible time.

-

-

-

-

-

- It consists of decluttering

It is unavoidable for our lives and living spaces to stack up a lot of junk over time. Such an amount of unnecessary belongings breed chaos and disorder in any once-upon-a-time sane living space. The Swedish death cleaning exercise will seek to do away with clutters of various forms, bringing back some degree of order into one's life and living space.

Do you have clutter in your living space? List out some things in your household which could be well-thought-out as clutters below.

-

-

-

-

-

- It Consists Of Decongesting

One's living space is always in danger of being congested. If nothing is done to any living space, it might become almost difficult to even live within that space as time goes on. The Swedish death cleaning exercise is known to initiate a purging of all living spaces, getting rid of congestion. After this exercise, one can breathe freely, as the fresh air permeates each space and life.

Do you suffer congestion in your life or within your living space? List out living spaces below which might necessitate decongestion.

-

-

-

-

-

- It Consists Of Reordering

As one gets more acquainted with living within spaces and with other people, there must arise at some point the need for order, and as time goes by, the need for reordering will also emerge. This is fundamental for leading a life of freedom and happiness. Embarking on the Swedish death cleaning will aid in the parting between what is essential and what isn't. Every step would reorder one's priorities, focus, and energy towards more productive ventures.

Do you see the need for reordering in your life or within your living space? List spaces below within your household that would require reordering.

-

-

-

-

-

What Swedish Death Cleaning Isn't

Ashley sat on the sofa in the living room, listening to every word her mother said. Her mom was educating her about the Swedish death cleaning, and so far, everything she had heard about the exercise was completely untrue.

"How did I miss this?" *Ashley thought,* "how did I end up with so much misinformation about this exercise?

"I agree I went too far in my quest to protect my mom from frauds who lurk around the elderly, all with the sole aim of ripping them off, but still, I should have sifted all that info properly to catch the truth." *Ashley continued her deep thinking, not hearing a word from her mother.*

"Ashley, are you listening to me, sweetheart?" her mom interjected.

"I'm so sorry, Mom, I got carried away for a sec. Please continue." Ashley said as she adjusted herself on her seat.

"Okay..." her mom continued, "now that I have clearly spelled out what the Swedish death cleaning exercise is to you, I would like to tell you what it is not.

"This will help you decipher the real thing from the fake stuff. Armed with this knowledge, we would be able to quickly lunch into the exercise and get tremendous results in no time!" Ashley's mom said with excitement.

"Wait.... we?" Ashley asked with surprise.

Owing to many misconceptions about the Swedish death cleaning exercise, one must be educated about what the exercise is not. This will further help in clearing any doubts and properly defining what is true from what is false. Once this is done, many people will see the value of such an exercise and will gladly embark on it without further procrastination.

Below are a few misconceptions about Swedish death cleaning.

- It is a Swedish Practice Meant for Only the Swedes

It is normal for people to associate the name of the cleaning method with the Swedes and/or that they are the only custodians of the practice and should be left to them and them alone. However, this is not the case at all. It is true that the cleaning method has its origin and was later popularised by the Swedes. It isn't solely a Swedish exercise or practice. Today, the Swedish death cleaning method has been adopted by many people as their preferred cleaning method; indeed, it has become popular worldwide.

Share below your thinking when you first heard of the name "Swedish death cleaning."

What did you think of the name "Swedish death cleaning?"

-

-

-

- It Is a Form of Swedish Ritual About Death.

The Swedish death cleaning clearly has nothing to do with pious or traditional rituals. It is purely a cleaning method that pursues freedom and happiness in one's life. The name might suggest a practice linked to some sort of ritualism or ethnic bias, but this is far from the truth. The only requirement needed for this exercise is one's availability, determination, time, and energy.

Share below what your thoughts were about the Swedish death cleaning sounding like something ritualistic or cultic.

-

-

-

- It Is a Practice only For Those With Terminal Diseases

This cleaning method is not solely to be practiced by people facing their imminent death in the near future. It is an exercise for everyone. Having the word death within its vocabulary isn't necessarily implied of an impending passing. For the elderly, once this exercise is carried out, it affords them freedom so they can spend their days in joy and happiness, whether they are still active or retired. In addition, releasing up space and income could lead to a healthier life. So, it is wrong to assume that anyone embarking on this cleaning method is sickly and heading to their grave. It would still be wrong to wait until one has been diagnosed with a terminal disease before urgently considering the need to carry out this cleaning method.

Share your thought on the word "death" in the vocabulary of this cleaning method. Did you think it was only for the dying?

-

-

-

A lot of other misconceptions abound about the Swedish death cleaning. Knowing them and enlightening one's mind in those regards is important. This will help in properly practicing the exercise.

Have you heard of any other forms of misconceptions about the Swedish death cleaning? Share them below and how you handled them.

-

-

-

-

Getting Started

Ashley stared at the paper handed to her by her mom. It had a list of things to do on it. She read each line carefully, letting out a sigh at intervals as she went through it.

"Mom, this exercise will take forever to finish!" Ashley said. "we practically have to put our lives at a standstill to get anywhere near the finish line."

Her mom looked at her and smiled while she kept scribbling on a dining table paper.

"You're funny, darling. Yes, it wouldn't be easy, but we would not have to put our active lives aside to achieve it. All it needs is a little planning, dedication, and faith." Ashley's mom said.

"But Mom, this is some serious exercise. We don't have enough tools to go by, we would need more hands, it would need our

endless commitment, and we might end up breaking down, all because we want a less-cluttered house!" Ashley said as she got irritated.

Her mom looked at her with a smile as she continued writing.

"Easy does it, darling. The big picture always begins with the first step." She said.

"What's the first step?"

If one looks at the exercise entirely, there might be some discouragement. It might all look overwhelming at first, but embarking on a task this massive would necessitate some pre-task preparation. It is not wise to simply up and begin doing everything at once, with no planning whatsoever. Such a move will only lead to quick fatigue, rapid diminution of one's enthusiasm, and subsequent botch from realising the expected outcomes. It is important to carry on with the exercise systematically if one wants to achieve success.

Before embarking on the Swedish death cleaning, here are a few things to have in mind.

- Begin with baby steps

There is no reason for taking a trip down memory lane, bemoaning why one didn't think to embark on the Swedish death cleaning earlier in life. Wasting time regretting one's past actions will not do any good. Junks will accumulate over time, and decisions might take longer than necessary to be arrived at and implemented. So, being too hard on one's self is needless. One needs to be mindful that self-criticism doesn't stand in the way of their passion and commitment in the long run. What is imperative is the step being taken NOW.

- Come up with a viable To-Do list

A to-do list is an itemised pool of things that one desires to get done. A to-do list is typically well-written and clearly outlined. Putting together this list is central to maintaining self-restraint and keeping track of one's progress. The primary purpose of a to-do list is to outline everything that one has to do, with the essential errands placed at the top of the list and the least important errands rooted at the bottom. By maintaining such a list, one ensures each errand is written all in one place. This will help, so nothing important is forgotten. A brief to-do list has been attached to this workbook to help with your Swedish death cleaning journey.

- Solicit assistance from friends and family

Like every meaningful endeavour, Swedish death cleaning is very demanding. However, such a task isn't insurmountable at all. All one has to do is include their loved ones as our family and friends are always eager to provide help. The ideas and input that such a company might offer may help cut down on expenses and waste, mitigating stress and any forms of hardship that may come up. Also, they might open the door for more creativity in carrying out the exercise.

- Rely on your wits

One thing that will definitely help you in this journey is the act of improvisation. Since the Swedish death cleaning would necessitate various actions such as boxing, packing, moving, and so on, it would be counterproductive if one goes acquiring more items as this may incur more cost and might add to the already cluttered space. Instead, use boxes and clear bags for packing items to the side.

- Don't overwork yourself. Take occasional time-outs

If care isn't taken, one might be tempted to over-indulge. Every act of enthusiasm must therefore be kept under control. Pushing one's self too hard might end up being counterproductive. Irrespective of one's intentions and drive towards achieving the desired feat, all cannot be accomplished in a single day. Regardless of how spirited one may feel, it is recommended that short breaks be taken in between hours. To avoid being carried away, one can employ the use of a timer or alarm. This will help with keeping you in check.

- Get rid of what is no longer needed. Not everything in the living space

The Swedish death cleaning is not an insensitive exercise. It does not seek to rid one of every possession that they have. In the quest to reduce clutter, one must know that it is okay to keep some valuable things. Everything valuable should be retained, while junk and needless items can be discarded. It will make no sense if everything within a space, valuable and surplus to requirements, is thoughtlessly removed in the name of cleaning. This is why the exercise must be carefully thought out and planned before execution to avoid throwing out the wrong things.

- Keep a detailed record of every activity for every day

It is important to be careful not to be caught in a vicious cycle of junks coming in and going out. This can be prevented by keeping a journal. Such documentation will help in sorting, delisting already cleaned-up boxes and spaces, and knowing which items and areas to focus on. Doing this will help with the overall advancement of the exercise and will save time and energy.

Thoughts to have in mind for a successful cleaning

A lot of thoughts will naturally go through one's mind while trying to organise their space. Below are a few tips that may come in handy when trying to achieve a successful Swedish death cleaning exercise. The objective is to offer guidance, not immovable guidelines. It is important that one is mindful not to slide down the undesirable path of inflexibility.

- Ask the right questions

A successful cleaning exercise will always be tailored around asking the most pertinent questions. The right answers will lead to pragmatic solutions that will greatly benefit the entire process.

"Do I need this?" "Why do I need it?" "How often do I use this?" "How much will I save if I get rid of this?" "What's the worse I could face if I let this go?"

Do you have pertinent questions that you would like to address? List any questions below that you might think as key in realising a successful cleaning exercise.

-

-

-

-

- Take courageous actions

Once the right questions begin to produce the right answers, such answers would necessitate corresponding actions. An instance may occur where one has emotional attachments to one item or the other. However, it is vital to take practical steps designed to help reach the goal in focus. A few items might be perplexing to get rid of because they are either gifts/presents and vintage goods or collectibles.

Are there tasks before you that would necessitate courageous actions? List items below within your home that you think would require boldness to get rid of.

-

-

-

-

- Put effort into planning

It is impossible to make any progress without appropriate, thoughtful planning, and it is ineffective for one to depend on their mental agility. A well-written outline has proven to be far more efficient than a sharp memory. It is wise to plainly write down what is required to achieve the set goals. Be sure to make a schedule and follow through on every detail. Planning should embody time frame, daily workload, and methods of removing unwanted items.

Have you put any thought into planning your exercise? List down below anything you would add in order to come up with a near-perfect plan.

-

-

-

-

-

CHAPTER 2

FORMULATING A TO-DO LIST

shley walks into the dining area and hands over a piece of paper to her mom, who is busy putting some of her thought down in writing.

"What's this, honey?" Her mom asked.

"It's the to-do list you asked me to put together. I did what I could, and... here we are." Ashley said.

Her mom took a glance at Ashley before looking at the paper, slowly reading its content.

"What's the matter, honey? You look somewhat distraught," Ashley's mom asked. "care to share?" she added.

"Well, going by what I wrote, I feel we have a long way to go in achieving anything with this Swedish death cleaning method. It's so cumbersome, tasking, busy and vague. Where on earth do we start?" Ashley asked while rolling her eyes.

Ashley's mom fixed her gaze on her daughter, smiled, then looked back at the paper in her hand.

"Where on earth do we start? I suppose our house would be the most appropriate." Ashley's mom said jokingly.

"Oh, be serious, mom!" Ashley said.

"Okay, we have to begin by rewriting your to-do list. Going by what I see here, there are quite a lot of things here that do nothing but add to your demotivation. If we rewrite the to-do list, however, we can eliminate vagueness. It's overall lack of excitement and zest." Ashley's mom said as she handed the paper back to her.

Ashely takes a long look at the to-do list, almost tearing it apart with her eyes. "okay, what makes a to-do list worth doing?" she asked

To-do lists are a fantastic way of keeping track of unsettled errands. However, they can be poor motivators as they repeatedly end up being too lengthy, short, ambiguous, unclear, over-committed, cumbersome, flat, misremembered, or even too carefully planned.

It might look as if coming up with a to-do list isn't an intricate deal, but it often is. Here are a few things to note while preparing a workable to-do list.

- Take note of the importance of each item on your to-do list

Typically, one's to-do list may feel like fetters, providing nothing but misery rather than motivation to finish the work. This is because, more often than not, one's to-do list comprises a collection of uninteresting, demanding, or prosaic tasks.

One way to handle this hurdle is to reframe one's list to center on bigger purposes. Connecting each task on one's to-do list to its bigger purpose will help minimize boredom while elevating motivation.

A quick way to do this is by adding a sentence to each task on the list, which clarifies the importance of carrying out that task. Once it can clearly define why a task must be done, there would be increased motivation to complete it.

- Remove tasks that have little or no value

Defining the value of each task on one's to-do list will help identify the tasks that aren't worth doing in all probability. Once the value provided b accomplishing a task cannot be determined, it is recommended that such a task be completely purged from the to-do list.

It is normal for a not-scrutinized to-do list to end up being overwhelming. Continuously adding new items to one's to-do list as they come up in one's head will often end up with dozens or hundreds of things to do.

It is important to parse through all of those items daily. This will help with the decision on what best to focus on next. Removing items of low value or no value that are only nice to do from one's list will help formulate a better to-do list as it makes one's list more practicable and less demanding. In addition, important tasks are prioritized, and distractions from less important tasks are eliminated.

- Make your to-do list progressive

It is possible that after one tries to streamline their to-do list by eliminating tasks with little or no value, they will still find the list overwhelming. It is at this point that one can contemplate using any or all of the following prioritisation methods for each week or day:

1. Begin each day by selecting between one and three tasks one would concentrate on throughout that day. The selected tasks would be the most important tasks. It is recommended that no other tasks should be attended to until those tasks are completed.
2. One can pick six tasks at the end of every workday; the selected tasks would be focused on the next day. They can be ordered in priority from one to six. On the scheduled day, those tasks can be worked on in the order of their priority until all six tasks are completed.
3. One can pick out 13 tasks at the beginning of every workday; the selected tasks would be focused on that day. Choose one high-priority task, three medium-priority tasks, and nine low-priority tasks. Endeavour to complete the high-priority task first, trailed by the medium-priority tasks, and finally the low-priority tasks.

One can complete these tasks at the end of each day or week. However, it would depend on the size of each task. In the event that one's chosen tasks take only a few hours to be achieved, then the daily schedule might be the best fit. But a weekly schedule would serve better if one has mostly multi-day tasks.

- Breakdown outsized to-dos tasks into smaller units

Having a list jam-packed with atrocious tasks that would take weeks to accomplish is one of the fastest ways to get overwhelmed when looking at one's to-do.

Let's say one of your tasks is "Declutter the attic." That's a colossal task composed of a lot of smaller tasks such as:

1. Cleaning out boxes
2. Cleaning out drawers and closets
3. Collecting valuables
4. Collecting the worthless (junk)
5. Collecting recyclables

By scrutinising the aforementioned, you will notice those tasks will require weeks of work, but all have been combined into a single to-do line item. As an alternative to having loads of very outsized tasks on one's lists, it is recommended that one spends quality time breaking those outsized tasks down into the smallest doable modules.

Such an action would make it easier to plan days and weeks ahead and also give one the pleasure of seeing more completed items on the to-do list. This will help in increasing motivation to keep working.

- Formulate a low-priority list

Your list may be overwhelmed with a lot of low-value tasks. However, such tasks may shoot up the priority table as the day or week goes by. It would be disheartening to you and your effort if all you do is delete such tasks earlier in the day or week, only for them to resurface with such a foremost priority. Therefore, it is recommended that another list be put together for low-priority tasks. The tasks on this list might not be urgent, but they might be doable when one has the time or go up the priority list. This will help keep your entire schedule of events organised and free from any forms of spring-up surprise.

Also, it is possible to squeeze some of these low-priority tasks into your day once you successfully complete your high-priority tasks on time. In addition, one can find that their reality seldom matches the plan they make ahead of time. Having a low priority list can help with striking a balance now and then.

- Subject your to-do list to public scrutiny

Allowing the input of others on your to-do list can help you plan it much better.

This action can have a lot of benefits. First, once one can have some extra eyes go through their to-do list, they will probably begin to see things they disregarded earlier when the list was remote. One might spot duplicate tasks which were included, tasks written as questions rather than actionable statements, and any poorly written tasks on the list.

Once mistakes are spotted, and the to-do list is re-written, one is compelled to consider each task, defining them better.

If no friend or family is accessible to go through one's planned to-do list, one can write their tasks as if they're going to be read by someone else. This will compel them to express and outline the tasks more clearly, making it easier and faster to act on them later.

- Employ the use of graphics for your to-do list

One most likely has the best chance of recalling what they need to do if they draw their to-do list instead of just writing each task down. Drawing or graphical representation employs a variety of unique skills. One has to envisage the item in their mind, ponder about its corporeal properties to figure out how to portray it in a drawing, and use their motor skills to draw it on the page. This combination may help create a stronger memory of the word. Drawing helps to generate a more interconnected memory trace that better incorporates visual, motor, and semantic information.

This method might best serve people who find that they are not getting enough done because they hardly recall what they have planned for the day. If attempted, one might be surprised at how much better they would recollect everything they wanted to get done.

If drawing isn't something one is good at, one can also try using a mind mapping tool to create more visual to-do lists.

The visual nature of a mind map will aid in creating a picture in one's mind of the things that need to be accomplished. One can also fasten images to their mind map for even more visual prompts to reference when they try to remember what needs to be accomplished.

To-Do List

Are there spaces within your household that need cleaning?

Write down four (4) items within such spaces that require cleaning.

Ante room

Living Room

Kitchen

Dining

Pantry

Master Bath Room

Other Bedrooms

Garage

Basement

Den

Study

Miscellaneous

CHAPTER 3

EMPLOYING CATEGORIZATION

shley opened the door to the attic. It swung in gently with a creaking sound. She and her mom walk into the room.

"Wow, this room hasn't been opened in forever," Ashley said as she waved her hand over her face to clear the dust.

"Not forever. I have been here several times this year." Ashley's mom said as she walked to the center of the room. They both looked around, glancing at the many kinds of stuff placed all around.

"So where do we start? This room might take us a whole month to clear out." Ashley said.

"No, it won't, not if we go about cleaning it the smart way." Ashley's mother said with a smile on her face.

"Okay, this room is our target space, according to the to-do list. We have broken each task into smaller units, and there is room for breaks here and there. How smarter can we get, mom?"

Ashley's mom then walked toward an old dresser in the corner of the room.

Ashley reluctantly followed her mom to the dresser, eager to hear what her mom wanted to say.

"Really, how so, mom?" Ashley inquired.

"We can begin with categorizing the items in this space, then spend time dealing with each category before moving on to the next." Ashley's mom said as she pulled the dresser's drawer open.

Ashley thought about what her mom had said, and a vivid picture began to form in her mind.

"You know what, mom, that sounds like a great idea. By going about it that way, we will be done with this space in no time!" Ashley said with excitement.

The Swedish death cleaning would employ different strategies, all geared towards making the exercise fun, easy and effective. One of which is the concept of categorisation.

Categorisation involves the cataloging, grouping, and labelling of each group of items within one's living space in preparation for proper disposal. This concept is essential as it can remove delays and muddles. This concept would ensure that items go to their desired termini when appropriately applied.

A few categories can be employed:

1. For gifting
2. For recycling
3. For keeping
4. For trashing
5. For donating

- For Gifting

Not all items within your selected living space are meant to be thrown away. Some may be good enough to be given away as gifts to family members and friends. Gifting away such items isn't a vulgar gesture at all. Putting items together as sets to be given out as gifts will aid with their proper storage before sending them out as gifts and with easy access to them when the time comes.

Do you have loved ones to whom you desire to gift some of your items? Do you possess items you feel are good enough to be offered as gifts to others?

. . .

List some of those items below within your home that you may wish to give out as gifts.

-

-

-

-

What are your reasons for wanting to gift out the items above?

-

-

-

-

- For Recycling

A lot of the items we possess within our homes are recyclable. This means that throwing them away wouldn't be the best thing to do, as they would only pollute our environment, hurting us in the long run. So, collect all recyclable items such as papers, plastics, and so on. Other items, such as wood, could be repurposed. These should be gathered in one place and transported to the recycling plants. It is important, however, that these recyclable items be collected and kept aside before notifying the recycling company, who would then come to cart them away.

. . .